WALT DISNEY PRODUCTIONS'

the Fox
and the
Hound

W9-BLT-739

IT IS A FOGGY SPRING MORNING WHEN THE OWL NAMED "BIG MAMA" STEPS OUT OF HER TREE HOME TO INVESTIGATE THE BAYING OF A PACK OF HOUNDS...

A FOX... RUNNING FROM THE HOUNDS!

ISBN-0-307-11292-6

BIG MAMA LEADS DINKY AND BOOMER TO THE LITTLE ORPHANED FOX...

JUST LOOK AT THAT POOR LITTLE GUY! HE NEEDS LOVE AND CARE!

ER... I'M NOT THE NURSE-MAID TYPE!

ME, NEITHER!

HEY! I'VE GOT A BIRD-BRAIN OF AN IDEA! FOLLOW ME!

LEAD ON, BIRDBRAIN... ER, BOOMER!

BIG MAMA, DINKY AND BOOMER ZOOM THROUGH THE MORNING MIST... THEIR MISSION—A LOVING HOME FOR THE FOX CUB.

THE WIDOW LOVES ANIMALS! SHE'S JUST THE ONE!

RAT-TAT-TAT!

YES? WHO'S THERE?

THAT'S STRANGE! I WAS SURE I HEARD SOMEONE KNOCKING AT MY DOOR!

SLAM!

OH, BOY ...THE STARS ARE OUT EARLY TODAY!

MY POOR BEAK WILL NEVER BE THE SAME!

OH, NO! THOSE PESTY BIRDS ARE FLYING OFF WITH MY LAUNDRY!

STOP! COME BACK WITH MY BLOOMERS!

BIG MAMA AND DINKY DROP THE BLOOMERS BESIDE A CERTAIN FENCE POST...

AND SO, BEFORE THE MORNING IS OVER, THE BIRDS HAVE FOUND THE BABY FOX A *NEW* HOME AND A *NEW* NAME.

LATER IN THE DAY, AMOS SLADE, THE WIDOW'S NEIGHBOR, WITH WHOM SHE OFTEN HAS DISAGREEMENTS, RETURNS TO HIS HOME.

CHIEF, OL' BOY, I'VE GOT A SURPRISE FOR YOU!

NOW TAKE IT EASY!

SNIFF!

HOW'S THIS FOR A HUNTIN' DOG?

YIP!

YAP!

THE HAIR BRISTLES ON CHIEF'S BACK...

I THOUGHT *I* WAS THE HUNTIN' DOG AROUND HERE!

THE PUP SCOOTS UNDER THE DISGRUNTLED CHIEF...

...AND MAKES HIMSELF AT HOME IN CHIEF'S BARREL.

UNDER THE WIDOW'S LOVING CARE, TOD GROWS RAPIDLY, ENJOYING THE RUN OF THE WHOLE FARM...

PHSST!

SQUEE!

SPLASH!

AND OFTEN AS NOT HIS "FUN" GETS HIM IN TROUBLE...

MOOOOO!

SWAT!

SWAT!

TOD! STOP PESTERING ABIGAIL!

THEN I'LL PICK ON SOMEBODY MY OWN SIZE!

BUT THE CHICKENS FIND IT HARD TO ENJOY A *FOX* AT CLOSE RANGE...EVEN *TOD*... AND ABIGAIL ENDS UP GETTING DISTURBED AGAIN...

SQUAWK! CLUCK! CLUCK!

MOOOOO!!

PEEP!

THE WIDOW GETS SWATTED...

SWAT!

SWISH!

AND TOD GETS DRENCHED IN "EXTRA RICH GRADE A".

SPLASH!

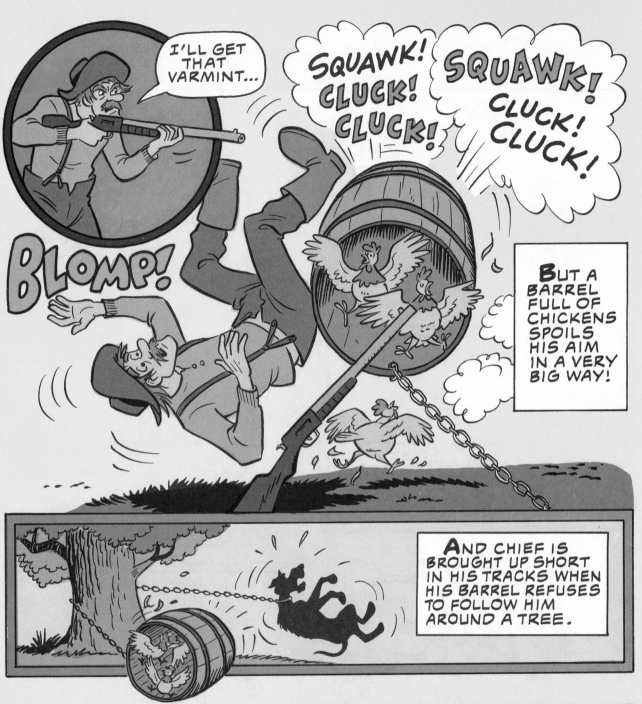

I'LL GET THAT VARMINT...

SQUAWK! CLUCK! CLUCK!

SQUAWK! CLUCK! CLUCK!

BLOMP!

BUT A BARREL FULL OF CHICKENS SPOILS HIS AIM IN A VERY BIG WAY!

AND CHIEF IS BROUGHT UP SHORT IN HIS TRACKS WHEN HIS BARREL REFUSES TO FOLLOW HIM AROUND A TREE.

IS IT SAFE NOW?

WELL, CHIEF IS BUSY... NURSING A SORE THROAT!

AMOS SLADE

AMOS SLADE

GOOD! I MEAN, IT'S GOOD THAT I CAN SHOW MY FACE AGAIN!

SPOTTING THE WIDOW ON HER WAY TO MARKET THE MILK, TOD RUNS TO OVERTAKE HER...

TH-THIS IS MY LAST CHANCE! I'M...I'M EXHAUSTED!

TOD!

TAKE THAT, YOU CHICKEN-CHASIN' VARMINT!

BLAM!

WHY, THAT HORRIBLE MAN SHOT MY MILK CANS!

HE'S GOING TO HEAR FROM ME...RIGHT NOW!

THE HUNTER HAS DIFFICULTY STARTING HIS TRUCK...

DAD BLAME IT, GET GOING!

AWK! CANTANKEROUS OL' TRUCK!

CHOOG!

NEVER HAS RUN RIGHT SINCE THE WIDOW SHOT IT!

KICK!

THE THOUGHT OF COPPER BEING AWAY FOR A LONG TIME CONCERNS TOD...

HE RACES ACROSS THE FIELDS TO BID FAREWELL TO HIS FRIEND.

BUT TOD ARRIVES TOO LATE...

COPPER! COPPER!

A-ROO! ROO-O!

I WANTED TO SAY GOODBYE TO MY FRIEND COPPER!

INDEED! AND WHAT DID YOU INTEND TO DO IF YOU RAN INTO OL' CHIEF?

AW, I CAN OUTFOX THAT OL' CHIEF DOG, BIG MAMA!

TCH-TCH! DIDN'T YOU LEARN ANYTHING FROM YOUR LAST ENCOUNTER, TOD?

♪ NOW IF YOU'RE SO FOXY ♪ THEN WHY DOES THAT HOUND AND OL' CHIEF'S SO DUMB, GET THE FOX ON THE RUN?

♪ 'CAUSE HE'S GOT THE HUNTER, AND THE HUNTER'S GOT THE GUN... KERBLAM!

YOU'D BETTER HOP OVER HERE TO THE HUNTER'S SHED, TOD, AND TAKE A PEEK!

THOSE SKINS COME FROM LACK OF EDUCATION...

KA-POW!

WHICH RESULTS IN ELIMINATION!

(GULP!) HOW AWFUL!

I'M SORRY, TOD HONEY, BUT IT'S TRUE! COPPER WILL COME BACK A TRAINED HUNTING DOG!

A REAL KILLER!

NO, NOT COPPER...HE WON'T EVER CHANGE! WE'RE FRIENDS FOREVER!

I HOPE YOU'RE RIGHT, TOD!

BUT FOREVER IS A LONG, LONG TIME... AND TIME HAS A WAY OF CHANGING THINGS!

I DON'T FEEL NOTHIN'!

SAME WITH ME!

MEANWHILE, SQUEEKS EXITS FROM THE NEXT SNOWDRIFT...

...AND HURRIES TOWARD THE WIDOW'S HOUSE, WHICH LOOKS WARM AND INVITING.

I GOT 'IM... I GOT 'IM... HUH? DINKY!?

DO I LOOK LIKE A WORM?

ER...ONLY YOUR TAIL PART!

OOPS! UNLESS MY EYES ARE PLAYIN' TRICKS...

I SEE A CATERPILLAR GOIN' THROUGH A KEYHOLE AT THE WIDOW'S HOUSE! C'MON!

HUMPH! LOOK AT THAT CRUMMY LI'L CREEP!

AND AS THE BIRDS FLY...

THAT'S THE WAY!

BLAM!

GOOD DOG! YOU DID JUST FINE!

I CAN SEE YOU'VE GOT A LOT OF NATURAL KNOW-HOW, COPPER!

PRACTICE, ALONGSIDE CHIEF, PERFECTS COPPER'S INNATE INSTINCTS... AND ALONG WITH GAINING KNOWLEDGE, COPPER GROWS IN SIZE...

AND WHEN THE TRAINING SEASON IS OVER, COPPER HAS EARNED THE HONOR OF SITTING "UP FRONT" WITH THE HUNTER...

YES, SIR, I'VE GOT ME THE TWO BEST HUNTIN' DOGS THERE IS!

COPPER'S A *HUNTING DOG* NOW, AND YOU'RE A *FOX!*

WELL, HONEY, DON'T GET YOUR HOPES TOO HIGH! THAT TRUCK IS PILED HIGH WITH SKINS THAT COPPER HELPED TRACK DOWN!

BUT I'VE JUST GOT TO FIND OUT IF HE'S STILL MY FRIEND!

AND THEN THERE'S OLD CHIEF...

I'LL BE CAREFUL! I'LL GO OVER TONIGHT WHEN CHIEF AND THE HUNTER ARE ASLEEP!

THAT NIGHT, COPPER, HAPPY TO BE HOME, IS FULL OF FUN...

C'MON, CHIEF... LET'S SCUFFLE!

DAGNABIT... LAY OFF, YOU OVERGROWN PUP!

AW, DON'T TREAT ME LIKE A PUP! I DID REAL GOOD TRACKIN' DOWN THOSE VARMINTS!

SMELLIN' AN' TRACKIN'S NOT ENOUGH... YA GOTTA *THINK NASTY,* TOO!

NOW LEAVE ME ALONE... I'M GOING TO SLEEP!

OKAY, CHIEF!

AND SHORTLY, TOD ARRIVES...

I THOUGHT THAT WAS YOU, TOD! I SAW YOU COMIN'! BOY, YOU'VE REALLY GROWN!

Z

YOU, TOO, COPPER! YOU'RE BIG!

BUT YOU SHOULDN'T HAVE COME... I...I'M A HUNTIN' DOG NOW!

HEY, LOOK... I JUST WANTED TO SEE YOU! WE'RE STILL FRIENDS, AREN'T WE?

POP!

HUH? A FOX IN OUR YARD!

CHIEF'S EXCITED ABOUT SOMETHIN'!

ROWF! ROWF!

OHO! A SASSY FOX! AFTER HIM, DOGS!

HEARTBROKEN, TOD RACES HOME TO THE WIDOW'S FARM...

OH, TOD...THANK HEAVEN YOU'RE SAFE!

BUT THE HUNTER SOON APPEARS, TO DELIVER AN ULTIMATUM...

WIDOW...YOUR FOX ALMOST KILLED CHIEF...AND I'M GOING TO GET HIM! YOU CAN'T KEEP HIM LOCKED UP FOREVER!

BAM! BAM!

IT IS THEN THAT THE WIDOW MAKES A FATEFUL DECISION...

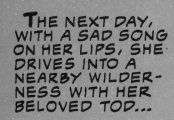

THE NEXT DAY, WITH A SAD SONG ON HER LIPS, SHE DRIVES INTO A NEARBY WILDERNESS WITH HER BELOVED TOD...

♪WE MET, IT SEEMS, SUCH A SHORT TIME AGO...YOU LOOKED AT ME, NEEDING ME SO...♪

♪YET FROM YOUR SADNESS OUR HAPPINESS GREW, AND I FOUND OUT I NEEDED YOU, TOO...♪

♪GOODBYE MAY SEEM FOREVER... FAREWELL IS LIKE THE END...BUT IN MY HEART'S THE MEMORY, AND THERE YOU'LL ALWAYS BE!♪

I'LL TAKE OFF YOUR COLLAR, TOD! YOU'LL BE SAFE HERE IN THIS GAME PRESERVE!

NO HUNTING

THE WIDOW TEARFULLY MAKES HER WAY TO HER CAR...

GOODBYE, TOD... GOODBYE!

SO FOR THE SECOND TIME IN HIS YOUNG LIFE, TOD EXPERIENCES THE EMPTY FEELING OF BEING ALONE.

AT DUSK, A BIG STORM RAPIDLY GATHERS FORCE...

I'D BETTER FIND SHELTER!

BOOM! CRASH!

THIS HOLLOW LOG WILL DO!

EXCUSE ME, MA'AM!

AHEM! THERE'S NO ROOM LEFT! ME AND MY BABIES FILL THIS PLACE!

YOU SAVED MY LIFE... AND MY MASTER'S, TOO!

WHEW! I'M TIRED... TOO TIRED TO MOVE!

THE HUNTER IS FREE OF HIS TRAP, AND...

CLICK!

GO ON, COPPER... MOVE OUT OF THE WAY...

BUT COPPER STANDS FIRM, PROTECTING HIS FRIEND, UNTIL THE GUN IS FINALLY LOWERED...

OH, ALL RIGHT! LET'S GO HOME!

I HAVE TO GO, TOD— BUT I'LL NEVER FORGET THIS DAY...OR YOU!

SO LONG, COPPER!

TOD IS SOON BACK WITH VIXEY... AND BOTH KNOW THEY WILL NEVER BE SEPARATED FROM EACH OTHER AGAIN...

AND A NEW LIFE ALSO STARTS TO UNFOLD FOR OTHERS...

MIGHTY NICE OF YOU TO PATCH UP MY FEET, WIDOW!

THEY'RE MENDING FINE, AMOS! YOU JUST NEED SOMEONE TO LOOK AFTER YOU!

WHILE NEARBY...

HUH? I THOUGHT WE HAD THE FUZZY WORM CORNERED IN THERE!

THOSE EYES...

SAY...DO YOU SUPPOSE... COULD IT BE...

COULDN'T BE...COULD IT??